THIS PLANNER

BELONGS TO:

_____

_____

PAGE	KEY CONTENT

PAGE	KEY CONTENT

PAGE	KEY CONTENT

PAGE	KEY CONTENT

Date ——————   Venue ——————

Time ——————   Duration ——————

CLASS THEME / MANTRA

Props	Music	Oils / Crystals

Notes   Feedback

☆☆☆☆☆

LESSON SEQUENCE

Date —————— Venue ——————

Time —————— Duration ——————

CLASS THEME / MANTRA

Props	Music	Oils / Crystals

Notes	Feedback
	☆☆☆☆☆

LESSON SEQUENCE

Date ———————

Time ———————

Venue ———————

Duration ———————

CLASS THEME / MANTRA

Props

Music

Oils / Crystals

Notes

Feedback

☆☆☆☆☆

LESSON SEQUENCE

Date ——————   Venue ——————

Time ——————   Duration ——————

CLASS THEME / MANTRA

Props	Music	Oils / Crystals

Notes   Feedback

☆☆☆☆☆

L E S S O N   S E Q U E N C E

Date ——————————

Time ——————————

Venue ——————————

Duration ——————————

CLASS THEME / MANTRA

Props

Music

Oils / Crystals

Notes

Feedback

☆☆☆☆☆

LESSON SEQUENCE

Date ——————

Time ——————

Venue ——————

Duration ——————

CLASS THEME / MANTRA

Props	Music	Oils / Crystals

Notes

Feedback

☆☆☆☆☆

LESSON SEQUENCE

Date ——————— Venue ———————

Time ——————— Duration ———————

CLASS THEME / MANTRA

Props	Music	Oils / Crystals

Notes	Feedback
	☆☆☆☆☆

LESSON SEQUENCE

Date ———————

Time ———————

Venue ———————

Duration ———————

CLASS THEME / MANTRA

Props

Music

Oils / Crystals

Notes

Feedback

☆☆☆☆☆

LESSON SEQUENCE

Date ———————

Time ———————

Venue ———————

Duration ———————

CLASS THEME / MANTRA

Props	Music	Oils / Crystals

Notes

Feedback

☆☆☆☆☆

LESSON SEQUENCE

Date ——————

Time ——————

Venue ——————

Duration ——————

CLASS THEME / MANTRA

Props	Music	Oils / Crystals

Notes

Feedback

☆☆☆☆☆

LESSON SEQUENCE

Date ——————

Time ——————

Venue ——————

Duration ——————

CLASS THEME / MANTRA

Props

Music

Oils / Crystals

Notes

Feedback

☆☆☆☆☆

LESSON SEQUENCE

Date ——————— Venue ———————

Time ——————— Duration ———————

CLASS THEME / MANTRA

Props	Music	Oils / Crystals

Notes	Feedback

☆☆☆☆☆

Date ———————   Venue ———————

Time ———————   Duration ———————

CLASS THEME / MANTRA

Props	Music	Oils / Crystals

Notes   Feedback

☆☆☆☆☆

LESSON SEQUENCE

Date _____   Venue _____

Time _____   Duration _____

CLASS THEME / MANTRA

Props   Music   Oils / Crystals

Notes   Feedback

☆☆☆☆☆

LESSON SEQUENCE

Date —————   Venue —————

Time —————   Duration —————

CLASS THEME / MANTRA

Props	Music	Oils / Crystals

Notes

Feedback

☆☆☆☆☆

LESSON SEQUENCE

Date ——————   Venue ——————

Time ——————   Duration ——————

CLASS THEME / MANTRA

Props	Music	Oils / Crystals

Notes   Feedback

☆☆☆☆☆

LESSON SEQUENCE

Date ——————

Time ——————

Venue ——————

Duration ——————

CLASS THEME / MANTRA

Props	Music	Oils / Crystals

Notes

Feedback

☆☆☆☆☆

LESSON SEQUENCE

Date ——————— Venue ———————

Time ——————— Duration ———————

CLASS THEME / MANTRA

Props	Music	Oils / Crystals

Notes

Feedback

☆☆☆☆☆

LESSON SEQUENCE

Date ———————

Time ———————

Venue ———————

Duration ———————

CLASS THEME / MANTRA

Props

Music

Oils / Crystals

Notes

Feedback

☆☆☆☆☆

LESSON SEQUENCE

Date ——————

Time ——————

Venue ——————

Duration ——————

CLASS THEME / MANTRA

Props

Music

Oils / Crystals

Notes

Feedback

☆☆☆☆☆

LESSON SEQUENCE

Date ——————

Time ——————

Venue ——————

Duration ——————

CLASS THEME / MANTRA

Props

Music

Oils / Crystals

Notes

Feedback

☆☆☆☆☆

LESSON SEQUENCE

Date —————— Venue ——————

Time —————— Duration ——————

CLASS THEME / MANTRA

Props	Music	Oils / Crystals

Notes   Feedback

☆☆☆☆☆

Date ———————   Venue ———————

Time ———————   Duration ———————

CLASS THEME / MANTRA

Props	Music	Oils / Crystals

Notes   Feedback

☆☆☆☆☆

LESSON SEQUENCE

Date ———————   Venue ———————

Time ———————   Duration ———————

CLASS THEME / MANTRA

Props	Music	Oils / Crystals

Notes   Feedback

☆☆☆☆☆

LESSON SEQUENCE

Date ———————   Venue ———————

Time ———————   Duration ———————

CLASS THEME / MANTRA

Props

Music

Oils / Crystals

Notes

Feedback

☆☆☆☆☆

LESSON SEQUENCE

Date _____   Venue _____

Time _____   Duration _____

CLASS THEME / MANTRA

Props   Music   Oils / Crystals

Notes   Feedback

☆☆☆☆☆

LESSON SEQUENCE

Date ―――――

Time ―――――

Venue ―――――

Duration ―――――

CLASS THEME / MANTRA

Props

Music

Oils / Crystals

Notes

Feedback

☆☆☆☆☆

Date ————————   Venue ————————

Time ————————   Duration ————————

CLASS THEME / MANTRA

Props	Music	Oils / Crystals

Notes   Feedback

☆☆☆☆☆

LESSON SEQUENCE

Date —————— Venue ——————

Time —————— Duration ——————

CLASS THEME / MANTRA

Props	Music	Oils / Crystals

Notes

Feedback

☆☆☆☆☆

LESSON SEQUENCE

Date ———————   Venue ———————

Time ———————   Duration ———————

CLASS THEME / MANTRA

Props   Music   Oils / Crystals

Notes   Feedback

☆☆☆☆☆

LESSON SEQUENCE

Date ———————   Venue ———————

Time ———————   Duration ———————

CLASS THEME / MANTRA

Props   Music   Oils / Crystals

Notes   Feedback

☆☆☆☆☆

LESSON SEQUENCE

Date ——————   Venue ——————

Time ——————   Duration ——————

CLASS THEME / MANTRA

Props   Music   Oils / Crystals

Notes   Feedback

☆☆☆☆☆

LESSON SEQUENCE

Date ——————

Time ——————

Venue ——————

Duration ——————

CLASS THEME / MANTRA

Props

Music

Oils / Crystals

Notes

Feedback

☆☆☆☆☆

LESSON SEQUENCE

Date ——————

Venue ——————

Time ——————

Duration ——————

CLASS THEME / MANTRA

Props

Music

Oils / Crystals

Notes

Feedback

☆☆☆☆☆

LESSON SEQUENCE

Date ———————

Time ———————

Venue ———————

Duration ———————

CLASS THEME / MANTRA

Props

Music

Oils / Crystals

Notes

Feedback

☆☆☆☆☆

LESSON SEQUENCE

Date ———————

Time ———————

Venue ———————

Duration ———————

CLASS THEME / MANTRA

Props

Music

Oils / Crystals

Notes

Feedback

☆☆☆☆☆

LESSON SEQUENCE

Date ——————

Time ——————

Venue ——————

Duration ——————

CLASS THEME / MANTRA

Props	Music	Oils / Crystals

Notes

Feedback

☆☆☆☆☆

LESSON SEQUENCE

Date ——————

Time ——————

Venue ——————

Duration ——————

CLASS THEME / MANTRA

Props

Music

Oils / Crystals

Notes

Feedback

☆☆☆☆☆

LESSON SEQUENCE

Date ——————— Venue ———————

Time ——————— Duration ———————

CLASS THEME / MANTRA

Props | Music | Oils / Crystals

Notes | Feedback

☆☆☆☆☆

LESSON SEQUENCE

Date ———————   Venue ———————

Time ———————   Duration ———————

CLASS THEME / MANTRA

Props	Music	Oils / Crystals

Notes   Feedback

☆☆☆☆☆

L E S S O N   S E Q U E N C E

Date ——————

Time ——————

Venue ——————

Duration ——————

CLASS THEME / MANTRA

Props

—————————
—————————
—————————
—————————
—————————
—————————
—————————

Music

—————————
—————————
—————————
—————————
—————————
—————————
—————————

Oils / Crystals

—————————
—————————
—————————
—————————
—————————
—————————
—————————

Notes

Feedback

☆☆☆☆☆

LESSON SEQUENCE

Date ———————

Time ———————

Venue ———————

Duration ———————

CLASS THEME / MANTRA

Props

Music

Oils / Crystals

Notes

Feedback

☆☆☆☆☆

LESSON SEQUENCE

Date ————   Venue ————

Time ————   Duration ————

CLASS THEME / MANTRA

Props	Music	Oils / Crystals

Notes   Feedback

☆☆☆☆☆

Date ——————

Time ——————

Venue ——————

Duration ——————

CLASS THEME / MANTRA

Props	Music	Oils / Crystals

Notes

Feedback

☆☆☆☆☆

LESSON SEQUENCE

Date ———————   Venue ———————

Time ———————   Duration ———————

CLASS THEME / MANTRA

Props   Music   Oils / Crystals

Notes   Feedback

☆☆☆☆☆

LESSON SEQUENCE

Date ——————— Venue ———————

Time ——————— Duration ———————

CLASS THEME / MANTRA

Props	Music	Oils / Crystals

Notes

Feedback

☆☆☆☆☆

LESSON SEQUENCE

Date ———————

Time ———————

Venue ———————

Duration ———————

CLASS THEME / MANTRA

Props

———————
———————
———————
———————
———————
———————
———————
———————

Music

———————
———————
———————
———————
———————
———————
———————
———————

Oils / Crystals

———————
———————
———————
———————
———————
———————
———————
———————

Notes

Feedback

☆☆☆☆☆

LESSON SEQUENCE

Date ——————

Time ——————

Venue ——————

Duration ——————

CLASS THEME / MANTRA

Props

Music

Oils / Crystals

Notes

Feedback

☆☆☆☆☆

LESSON SEQUENCE

Date ——————

Time ——————

Venue ——————

Duration ——————

CLASS THEME / MANTRA

Props

Music

Oils / Crystals

Notes

Feedback

☆☆☆☆☆

LESSON SEQUENCE

Date ——————

Time ——————

Venue ——————

Duration ——————

CLASS THEME / MANTRA

Props

Music

Oils / Crystals

Notes

Feedback

☆☆☆☆☆

LESSON SEQUENCE

Date ——————

Time ——————

Venue ——————

Duration ——————

CLASS THEME / MANTRA

Props	Music	Oils / Crystals

Notes

Feedback

☆☆☆☆☆

LESSON SEQUENCE

Date ———————

Time ———————

Venue ———————

Duration ———————

CLASS THEME / MANTRA

Props

Music

Oils / Crystals

Notes

Feedback

☆☆☆☆☆

LESSON SEQUENCE

Date ——————

Time ——————

Venue ——————

Duration ——————

CLASS THEME / MANTRA

Props

Music

Oils / Crystals

Notes

Feedback

☆☆☆☆☆

LESSON SEQUENCE

Date ——————

Time ——————

Venue ——————

Duration ——————

CLASS THEME / MANTRA

Props	Music	Oils / Crystals

Notes

Feedback

☆☆☆☆☆

LESSON SEQUENCE

Date ———————   Venue ———————

Time ———————   Duration ———————

CLASS THEME / MANTRA

Props	Music	Oils / Crystals

Notes   Feedback

☆☆☆☆☆

Date ———————

Time ———————

Venue ———————

Duration ———————

CLASS THEME / MANTRA

Props

Music

Oils / Crystals

Notes

Feedback

☆☆☆☆☆

LESSON SEQUENCE

Date ———————

Time ———————

Venue ———————

Duration ———————

CLASS THEME / MANTRA

Props

Music

Oils / Crystals

Notes

Feedback

☆☆☆☆☆

LESSON SEQUENCE

Date ———————

Time ———————

Venue ———————

Duration ———————

CLASS THEME / MANTRA

Props

Music

Oils / Crystals

Notes

Feedback

☆☆☆☆☆

LESSON SEQUENCE

Date ——————

Time ——————

Venue ——————

Duration ——————

CLASS THEME / MANTRA

Props

Music

Oils / Crystals

Notes

Feedback

☆☆☆☆☆

LESSON SEQUENCE

Date ——————

Time ——————

Venue ——————

Duration ——————

CLASS THEME / MANTRA

Props	Music	Oils / Crystals

Notes

Feedback

☆☆☆☆☆

LESSON SEQUENCE

MOTIVATIONAL QUOTES FOR YOGA CLASS

"The perfect metaphor for life. In yoga, it's all about the journey, not the destination. It's about what happens at each step along the way and how it changes and moves you"

"We must be willing to let go of the life we planned so as to have the life that is waiting for us." – Joseph Campbell

"Yoga teaches us to cure what need not be endured and endure what cannot be cured." – B.K.S. Iyengar

"The highest spiritual practice is self-observation without judgment." – Swami Kripalu

"Your task is not to seek for love but merely to seek and find all barriers within yourself that you have built against it." –Rumi

"Your present circumstances don't determine where you can go, they merely determine where you start." – Nido Qubien

"Every thought you produce, anything you say, any action you do, it bears your signature." – Thich Nhat Hanh, Buddhist monk

"The privilege of a lifetime is to become who you truly are." – Carl Jung

"To be yourself in a world that is constantly trying to make you someone else is the greatest accomplishment." – Ralph Waldo Emerson

"Yoga is the journey of the self. Through the self. To the self." – The Bhagavad Gita

MOTIVATIONAL QUOTES FOR YOGA CLASS

"Perfect courage is to do without witnesses what one would be capable of doing with the world looking on." – Francois de La Rochefoucauld

"Open your eyes, look within. Are you satisfied with the life you're living? "
— Bob Marley

"Every moment is a fresh beginning. "— T.S. Eliot

No man ever steps in the same river twice, for it's not the same river and he's not the same man." – Heraclitus

Go confidently in the direction of your dreams. Live the life you have imagined. — Henry David Thoreau

"If you hear a voice within you say, "you cannot paint," then by all means paint and that voice will be silenced." — Vincent Van Gogh

"Start where you are. Use what you have. Do what you can. "— Arthur Ashe

"The difference between ordinary and extraordinary is that little extra. "— Jimmy Johnson

"No one saves us but ourselves. No one can and no one may. We ourselves must walk the path. "— Buddha

"The journey of a thousand miles begins with one step. "– Lao Tzu

MOTIVATIONAL QUOTES FOR YOGA CLASS

"The power of imagination makes us infinite. "— John Muir

"The only person you are destined to become is the person you decide to be. "— Ralph Waldo Emerson

"When I let go of what I am, I become what I might be." — Lao Tzu

"In the midst of winter, I found there was, within me, an invincible summer." — Camus

"Everything is energy and that's all there is to it. Match the frequency of the reality you want and you cannot help but get that reality. It can be no other way. This is not philosophy. This is physics. "– Albert Einstein

"Everything you've ever wanted is on the other side of fear... "– George Addair

" When one door of happiness closes, another opens, but often we look so long at the closed door that we do not see the one that has been opened for us." – Helen Keller

"Make each day your masterpiece. "– John Wooden

"Life is not measured by the number of breaths we take, but by the moments that take our breath away." — Maya Angelou

"Light tomorrow with today. – Elizabeth Barrett Browning"

MOTIVATIONAL QUOTES FOR YOGA CLASS

"We can easily forgive a child who is afraid of the dark; the real tragedy of life is when men are afraid of the light. "– Plato

"Thousands of candles can be lighted from a single candle, and the life of the candle will not be shortened. Happiness never decreases by being shared. "– Buddha

"People often say that motivation doesn't last. Well, neither does bathing. That's why we recommend it daily. "– Zig Ziglar

"Even the darkest night will end and the sun will rise." – Victor Hugo

"Yoga is not a work-out, it is a work-in. And this is the point of spiritual practice; to make us teachable; to open up our hearts and focus our awareness so that we can know what we already know and be who we already are." – Rolf Gates

"Dreaming, after all, is a form of planning." – Gloria Steinem

"I close my eyes in order to see." – Paul Gauguin

"Yoga is the practice of tolerating the consequences of being yourself." – Bhagavad Gita

"You miss 100% of the shots you don't take. "— Wayne Gretzky

"There is only one corner of the universe you can be certain of improving, and that's your own self. "— Aldous Huxley